CRASSULAS IN CULTIVATION

By the same author

SUCCULENTS IN CULTIVATION
THE STUDY OF CACTI
SUCCULENT PLANTS ILLUSTRATED
CACTUS GROWING FOR BEGINNERS
CACTI FOR DECORATION

CRASSULAS
IN
CULTIVATION

VERA HIGGINS, M.A., V.M.H.

with colour and line illustrations by the author

LONDON

BLANDFORD PRESS

First published 1964
© 1964 Blandford Press Ltd.,
167 High Holborn, London, W.C.1.

Printed in Great Britain by Richard Clay and Company, Ltd.,
Bungay, Suffolk

Contents

List of Colour Illustrations   7

List of Line Drawings   9

1 INTRODUCTION   11

2 CULTIVATION   15

3 CLASSIFICATION   17

4 NAMES CONFUSED AND MISUSED   20

5 DESCRIPTION OF SPECIES IN CULTIVATION   24

Appendix: Authors of Botanical Names   73

Index   77

Colour Illustrations

		Facing Page
Plate		
1 a	C. alstonii	12
b	C. cooperi	
c	C. anomala	
d	C. columnaris	
e	C. columella	
f	C. barbata	
g	C. argyrophylla	
2 a	C. capensis	15
b	C. comptonii	
c	C. cornuta	
d	C. falcata	
e	C. deceptrix	
3 a	C. gillii	30
b	C. hystrix	
c	C. laticephala	
d	C. intermedia	
e	C. hemisphaerica	
4 a	C. nemorosa	33
b	C. marginalis	
c	C. mesembryanthoides (syn. trachysantha)	
d	C. mesembrianthemopsis (syn. rapacea)	
e	C. obvallata	
5 a	C. orbicularis	48
b	C. triebneri	
c	C. quadrangula	
d	C. quadrangularis	
e	C. perforata	
6 a	C. portulacea	51
b	C. pyramidalis	
c	C. platyphylla	

		Facing Page
Plate		
7 *a*	*C. brevifolia*	66
b	*C. rupestris*	
c	*C. rupestris*	
d	*C. rupestris*	
8 *a*	*C. tecta*	69
b	*C. schoenlandii* (syn. *mesembryanthemoides*)	
c	*C. teres*	
d	*C. radicans*	
e	*C. socialis*	
f	*C. saxifraga*	

Line Drawings

Fig.		Page
1	Types of Flower	17–19
2	C. alpestris	25
3	C. arborescens	26
4	C. arta	26
5	C. ausiensis	27
6	C. cephalophora	29
7	C. ciliata	30
8	C. clavifolia	30
9	C. conjuncta	34
10	C. cooperi	35
11	C. corallina	36
12	C. cordata	37
13	C. corymbulosa	38
14	C. dasyphylla	39
15	C. deltoidea	40
16	C. eendornensis	41
17	C. erosula	42
18	C. fragilis	43
19	C. grisea	45
20	C. interrupta	46
21	C. lactea	48
22	C. lanuginosa	51
23	C. lycopodioides	52
24	C. marnierana	52
25	C. milfordae	54
26	C. multicava	55
27	C. nealeana	56
28	C. pellucida	58
29	C. perforata	59
30	C. portulacea var. obliqua	60
31	C. punctulata	61
32	C. reversisetosa	62

9

LINE DRAWINGS

Fig.		Page
33	*C. rosularis*	63
34	*C. sarcocaulis*	64
35	*C. schmidtii*	65
36	*C. spathulata*	66
37	*C. subaphylla*	69
38	*C. tetragona*	70
39	*C. tomentosa*	72

CHAPTER 1

Introduction

THE Family *Crassulaceae* includes a number of plants that are well-known in gardens; a few of them are hardy in the British Isles while others need the protection of a greenhouse, at least during the winter months. The *Sempervivums* are well known and much used in rock gardens, and many members of the closely allied genus *Sedum* are also hardy, although some of them need warmer conditions. *Cotyledons* and especially *Echeverias*, which were formerly included in *Cotyledon*, are often used for bedding out in the summer on account of their beautifully coloured leaves, while there are a number of attractive plants for the greenhouse among the *Bryophyllums* and *Kalanchoes*, all now regarded as belonging to the latter genus. People who grow succulent plants are also interested in *Adromischus* (formerly included in *Cotyledon*) as well as in *Rosularia*, *Umbilicus* and *Monanthes*, but the genus that includes the greatest variety and the one from which the family takes its name is *Crassula*.

There are over 200 species of *Crassula* known, most of them occurring naturally in Southern Africa, and of these between seventy and eighty are, or have been, in cultivation. They vary from annuals and the well-known *C. lycopodioides* among the simplest types, through the shrubby forms to the compact, very succulent plants which are found in desert areas. The flowers are always small and, as a rule, not very showy, though *C. falcata*, with its large, flat head of scarlet flowers topping a tall stem decorated with greyish, sickle-shaped leaves, is very handsome.

The general characteristics of the genus are that the leaves are always arranged in pairs alternating up the stem; the distance between the leaf-pairs may be long in the shrubby types, but in others, where the internodes are short, the plants form four-sided rosettes or columns. The flowers are generally borne in branched inflorescences with longer or shorter stems, each terminating in a compact cluster of flowers, though in some of the highly adapted species they are stemless, in a close bunch at the top of the main stem—shaving-brush type; such plants die after flowering unless there are lower branches which have not yet flowered.

Many Crassulas are quite easy to identify, but others are more difficult because of the variations that occur between different specimens; this may be due to hybridisation, incorrect cultivation or, in nature, if the plants are distributed over a wide area there may be variations due to the different climatic conditions in which they occur. The size and structure of the flower would not vary much, but the leaves may easily be thicker or thinner than the type, nearer or farther apart, more or less hairy, with colour variations also, those from the drier regions being less green than those from moister places. Enough living material has reached this country to show that certain species, for example *C. rupestris*, *C. perforata* and others, have a very wide range of variation, and should be regarded as polymorphic from the botanical point of view. The gardener, however, will recognise types distinct in some character that is important to him—colour and shape of leaves, colour of flowers and even in the flowering time. Where such variants are sufficiently distinct and are vegetatively propagated, a horticultural name may be desirable, and it is hoped that cultivar names will be given in such cases, since this would avoid the overloading of the classification with botanical names of doubtful application.

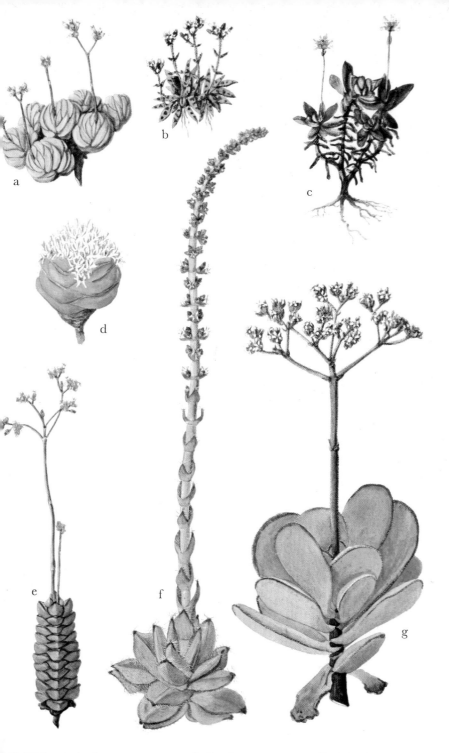

PLATE 1   a) *C. alstonii*   d) *C. columnaris*   f) *C. barbata*
          b) *C. cooperi*   e) *C. columella*   g) *C. argyrophylla*
          c) *C. anomala*

PLATE 2 a) *C. capensis*   c) *C. cornuta*   e) *C. deceptrix*
                b) *C. comptonii*   d) *C. falcata*

CHAPTER 2

Cultivation

CRASSULAS are not difficult to grow; even the small, very succulent species present no great difficulties and are not nearly so fastidious as, for instance, the mimicry Mesembryanthemums, which may need to be kept completely dry for several months, the period of the year when this is required depending on the species. But most Crassulas can be given a reasonable amount of water throughout the year, rather more when flower buds are developing and rather less after flowering. It is sometimes said that they like a sunny position, and this is true of most Crassulas, but some of the plants with thinner leaves do not like full sun and are usually found in nature on the shady side of rocky slopes. Since our sunshine never approaches that of South Africa, plants whose requirements are not known precisely can be tried in full sun in a greenhouse, as this brings out the colour which some species develop in stem or leaf, but if the plants wilt easily or the leaves get burnt, then they should be put in the shade of larger plants.

A few Crassulas are hardy in this country and will even stand some frost, but the majority grow best in a light greenhouse where the temperature does not fall below 40° F. (6° C.); they should be quite safe on the window-sill of a living-room.

If the plants are grown in a greenhouse the usual porous clay pots or pans are suitable and, to prevent them drying out in the hot sun, they may be sunk in ash or sand on the staging. A similar effect can be got with plastic pots that have drainage holes; these need not be plunged, since no water passes through the sides, but they need much less watering than porous pots. China or plastic pots or bowls, without drainage holes, can be used in living-rooms, and a selection of plants can be grown together in them; provided a good layer of crocks or pebbles is

B

put on the bottom below the potting soil, they will last in good condition for several years if not over-watered.

The soil used should be open and rather sandy. John Innes Potting Compost with the addition of coarse sand will suit most Crassulas, though a slightly richer compost can be used for those plants whose leaves are not so succulent; a little peat or leaf-mould added would be all that they require.

All Crassulas can be propagated from leaves which, if pulled off close to the main stem, root easily; if larger plants are wanted in a shorter time they can be grown from cuttings. Seed is often produced and germinates freely, but, in a greenhouse, there is always the possibility that hybridisation may have taken place, and the seedlings should not be given the parental name until it is certain that they resemble their parents in all particulars.

Crassulas do not suffer much from pests and diseases. The occasional mealy bug should be removed as soon as seen, but they are not a serious trouble; the woody species sometimes get scale insects, but these also can be brushed or picked off as soon as seen. Spraying with an insecticide is best avoided, since it may damage the surface of the leaves which, in many cases, are covered with wax.

Among the species that flower during the winter months and therefore need less water during the summer are: *C. deceptrix*, *C. gillii*, *C. grisea*, *C. lactea*, *C. lycopodioides*, *C. mesembrianthemopsis*, *C. multicava*, *C. nealeana*, *C. nemorosa*, *C. portulacea*, *C. rupestris* (some forms), *C. tecta*.

CHAPTER 3

Classification

FOR those who are interested in the relationships between the species, the seven Sections into which the Crassulas are divided are briefly summarised. The classification is made chiefly on the form of the flower, the parts of which are normally in fives, but may occasionally be in fours or sixes; the sepals are nearly free at the base and shorter than the petals, which may be free or united for a short distance; they are often white, but may be pink, red or yellow.

In the more primitive types the petals are arranged like a star; in the more highly developed species they may be erect with the tips recurved. In many cases there is a small outgrowth behind the tip of each petal which is known as a mucro. The stamens are usually shorter than the petals, and the carpels may be short or elongated, generally free, in the upper part at least; each is accompanied by a small scale (or squama) which varies in size, shape or colour in the different species and is typical of the Family *Crassulaceae*.

Section I. TILLAEOIDEAE. Found all over South Africa, but mostly in the South-West Cape Province. Many of the species are small annuals growing in moist or even marshy places and are not in cultivation, but a few of the more advanced types are well known, such as *C. corallina*, *C. dasyphylla* and *C. lycopodioides*.

Section II. STELLATAE. Mostly in the coastal range of South Africa. The species included here are perennial plants with succulent stems and leaves, sometimes forming large shrubs; examples are: *C. arborescens* and *C. portulacea*, as well as semi-shrubs such as *C. lactea* and *C. marginalis*. The flowers are stellate, the petals united at the base only and the squamae are minute.

FIG. 1 *a*—Section II. Stellatae.

Section III. TUBEROSAE. Chiefly found in damp rock crevices in South-West Cape Province, extending into Natal. These species are unusual in having tuberous roots from which the leaves and flowers arise annually; a few, such as *C. nemorosa* and *C. capensis*, are in cultivation, but they are uncommon.

Section IV. CAMPANULATAE.
Found all over South Africa and even extending into Tropical Africa. This is the largest Section, and includes many of the best known *Crassulas* in cultivation. The petals are generally erect, curved outwards at the tip with a small mucro behind. Some of the species are rosette plants, others have woody stems and the leaves are markedly succulent. Examples are: *C. rupestris, C. sarcocaulis, C. falcata, C. socialis* and *hemisphaerica*, as well as almost stemless plants *C. arta* and *C. deceptrix*.

FIG. 1 *b*—Section IV.
Campanulatae.

Section V. SPHAERITIS. The species in this Section are confined to Cape Province. The flowers are small, the petals erect, folded up the centre with the tips recurved but generally without a mucro. Examples are: *C. comptonii, C. tecta* and *C. hystrix*.

Section VI. GLOBULEA. Widely distributed in dry localities of Cape Province, Namaqualand and Basutoland. The plants vary in form, but the flowers, generally crowded into dense heads on slender stems, are typical; the petals are united at the base, incurved at the tip and have a large, subglobular mucro on the back. The best-known species are *C. anomala, C. radicans, C. obvallata* and *erosula*.

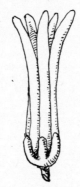

FIG. 1 *c*—Section V.
Sphaeritis.

FIG. 1 *d*—Section VI.
Globulea.

Section VII. PYRAMIDELLA. Chiefly found in the Karroo, in Central and Western Cape Province. This section shows the highest development in the Family; the leaf-pairs are generally close together, forming a column, and the flowers are bunched in stemless heads at the top; the petals are joined into a tube at the base, erect but without a mucro. Examples are: *C. columnaris, C. pyramidalis* and *C. teres.*

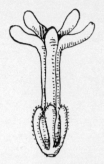

Fig. 1 *e*—Section VII. Pyramidella.

In the alphabetical list of species that follows the Section to which each plant belongs is indicated by a Roman numeral after the name of the plant.

CHAPTER 4

Names Confused and Misused

C. abyssinica. This name is sometimes found attached to plants which are *C. perfoliata* or hybrids of that species. The true *C. abyssinica* A. Rich. comes from Tropical Africa, Eritraea and Abyssinia; it has leaves in a basal rosette, from which rises a leafy inflorescence 20–30 in. (50–75 cm.) high and is now known by its earlier name, *C. alba* Forsk., which leads to a further confusion, as the name *C. alba* Hort. is a synonym of *C. albiflora* Sims.

C. argentea. This name had fallen into disuse until Schonland revived it after examining the type specimen of *C. argentea* in Thunberg's Herbarium, but it is more probable that that specimen is *C. arborescens* (Mill.) Willd.; therefore the name *C. argentea* should not be used, as the identity of the plant intended is uncertain.

C. coccinea. It is not uncommon to find plants in florists' shops labelled *Crassula coccinea*, though actually they belong to the genus *Rochea*, which formerly included other plants that are now classed as *Crassulas*, such as *Rochea falcata* and *R. perfoliata*, whose correct names now are *Crassula falcata* Wendl. and *C. perfoliata* L.

C. corallina, C. dasyphylla and **C. simiana.** There are only two plants concerned here, but they have been confused. *C. corallina* was described by Thunberg and is a plant with a tap root, from which arise several short stems bearing little, waxy, white leaves. Harvey described a similar plant as *C. dasyphylla*, but no mention was made of the tap root, though he did say that plants collected by Zehyer were stouter and had a large woody root. In 1897 Schonland described a similar plant as *C. simiana*, but later said it could not be distinguished from *C. corallina*, which he regarded as the same as *C. dasyphylla*. It is now known that two plants are involved: *C. corallina* Thunb., which grows in the dry desert regions of Namaqualand and *C. dasyphylla* Harv. from farther east in a less arid climate. The plants are similar, but in *corallina* there is a tap root and the branches do not root down, while *dasyphylla* usually has greener leaves, no tap root and the branches are prostrate, rooting along their length. There is also a difference in their floral structure.

C. deltoidea. This specific name was originally given by Thunberg to a plant later named *C. rhomboidea* by N. E. Brown, but the earlier name has priority. Harvey used the name *deltoidea*, but for a different plant which Schonland later renamed *C. arta.*

C. mesembryanthemoides, etc. The resemblance of several species of Crassula to various Mesembryanthemums has resulted in several of them being given names indicative of this fact. The spelling is also somewhat confused. The name *Mesembrianthemum* was first used by Breyne for plants of that genus; it means a midday flower, but the spelling was altered to *Mesembryanthemum* by Dillenius when night-flowering species were discovered; the meaning is 'pistil in centre of flower', which is rather vague and applicable to a very large number of flowering plants. However, in 1753 Linnaeus adopted the spelling with a 'y' and, in accordance with the International Rules of Botanical Nomenclature, this is the correct form.

C. mesembryanthoides Haw. D. Dietr. was the earliest name given to the small shrubby *Crassula* with bristly leaves known to many people as *C. trachysantha* and therefore has precedence.

C. mesembrianthoides Schon. et Bak. f., being the same as the name given above but used at a later date for a different plant, can no longer be used, and this plant has been renamed *C. schoenlandii* by Jacobsen. The same applies to the name *C. mesembryanthemoides* Dint. et Berg., which is a synonym for the same plant, which should therefore also be *C. schoenlandii* Jacobs.

C. mesembrianthemopsis Dinter, a charming little rosette plant, was later named by Schonland *C. rapacea*, but this name is not needed.

C. obliqua and **C. portulacea** may be considered together. The name *portulacea* was given by Lamarck in 1786 to plants grown in Europe; *C. obliqua* is a very similar shrub and was described three years later in Aiton's *Hortus Kewensis* from plants brought from South Africa by Masson. These two plants resemble each other in their method of growth, but the leaves of *portulacea* are rounder and, if grown hard, red edged, while those of *obliqua* remain green, are more pointed and sometimes twisted slightly. There is a horticultural distinction between these plants, for, when large enough, *C. portulacea* flowers well in England while *C. obliqua* does not. Since *C. portulaceae* is well known in South Africa and *C. obliqua* is not known there in the wild, it is probably best to regard it as a variety under the name *C. portulacea* var. *obliqua*. There are a number of variations in cultivation which, if sufficiently distinct, should be given clonal names.

C. perfossa. This is another name that should not be used, since it has been applied to two distinct plants. The name was first given by Lamarck, but he had not seen the flowers, and later it was regarded as a synonym of *C. perforata*; but in Harvey's *Flora Capensis* the name *perfossa* is given to a plant whose description fits that of *C. rupestris*, although that species is listed by Harvey as 'unknown'. There are two distinct plants which can easily be distinguished when in flower—*C. perforata* Thunb., which has a long, slender, branching inflorescence of small yellow flowers, and *C. rupestris*, which has a compact corymb of white or pink flowers terminating the stem. In both plants the leaves are united in pairs embracing the stem and vary in size and thickness, but normally in *C. perforata* they are thinner and may have a ciliate edge, while those of *C. rupestris* are usually much thicker and do not have the ciliate edge. The confusion in the names is partly due to the fact that Harvey described *C. rupestris* under the name *C. perfossa* and gave *C. rupestris* in his list of 'Doubtful species unknown to me', although it is a very common plant in South Africa.

C. quadrangula and **C. quadrangularis** are quite distinct plants despite the similarity of the names. *C. quadrangula* closely resembles *C. pyramidalis*, but it is larger and does not branch, while *C. quadrangularis* Schonl. forms compact rosettes of short, pointed leaves, wide at the base, from the centre of which the flower stems arise.

C. turrita. The plant to which this name is occasionally attached is a form of *C. lycopodioides*; the name was used in earlier days by Haworth for *C. barbata* Thunb. Since there is no specimen of *C. turrita* in Thunberg's herbarium, it is difficult to decide what plant was intended.

CHAPTER 5

Description of Species in Cultivation

This list does not claim to be complete, but it is hoped that it includes a sufficient number of the species generally met with in cultivation to be helpful to growers of these plants. For the benefit of those who are interested in the relationships between the different types, the name of the person who first described the species is given; the Roman figure refers to the Section to which the plant belongs (see Chapter 3).

C. alpestris Thunb. VII. (*A. alpestris* Harv. is a distinct plant, now known as *C. harveyi* Britt. et Bak.) Cape Province.

A small plant, the stem simple or branching, with close-packed, triangular leaves, ciliate at the edge, the tips recurved. Flowers white, in a close head at the top of each stem. Allied to *C. pyramidalis*, but less compact and the stems do not die after flowering.

C. alstonii Marl. IV. Namaqualand. Plate 1, *a*.

A small rosette plant, branching at the base; the leaves are wider than long, incurved, grey-green, slightly succulent, forming oval rather than circular rosettes. The little white flowers are carried on slender stems some 2 in. high, in small branching cymes.

C. anomala Schon. et Bak. f. V. South-West Cape Province and Basutoland. Plate 1, *c*.

A small, woody, branching shrub with slightly fleshy leaves crowded at the top of each branch, dark green or reddish. Flowers small, in crowded cymes on long, slender stems. If grown hard in full sun the whole plant becomes red, as it is in nature.

C. arborescens (Mill.) Willd. II. Cape Province.

A shrubby plant growing 7–8 ft. high in nature; the stems are

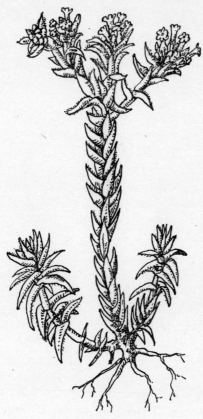

FIG. 2—*C. alpestris.*

stout and woody, the leaves broad, narrowing to the base, grey-green with reddish dots on the upper surface and a red edge. The flowers are star-shaped, pink, in a close panicle, but they are seldom produced in this country; there is, however, a record in the *Botanical Magazine*, Pl. 384 (1797), that it had flowered at the Chelsea Garden, though neither Miller nor Aiton had seen it in blossom. It was at first thought to be a *Cotyledon*.

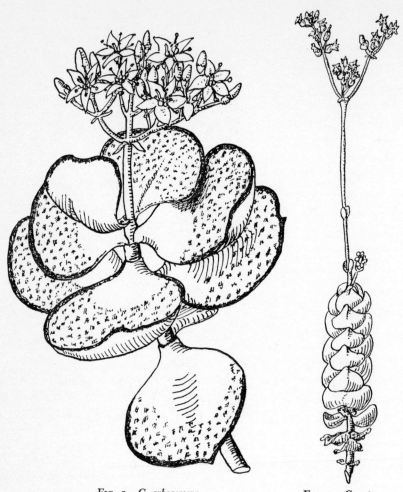

FIG. 3—*C. arborescens*.   FIG. 4—*C. arta*.

C. argentea Thunb.

The plant intended by Thunberg is so uncertain, and Harvey in *Flora Capensis* lists it as 'unknown'. The name was used by Linnaeus, but the herbarium specimen looks rather like *C. arborescens*. Schonland considered that the name should be applied to *C. portulacea* Lam., and it is sometimes so used in cultivation, but, owing to the uncertainty surrounding it, the name is best discarded (see Chapter 4).

C. argyrophylla Diels. IV. Transvaal, Pretoria and Rhodesia. Plate 1, *g*.

A low-growing plant with woody stems; the leaves are large, broad and rounded at the tip, narrowing to the base, the edges usually ciliate, held in a loose rosette, from the centre of which rises the inflorescence, some 6 in. or more high, branching at the top. Flowers small, white.

C. arta Schonl. (Synonym, *C. deltoidea* Harv.) IV. Cape Province.

A small, compact plant branching from the base; the short, wide, pointed, succulent leaves are closely packed together to form a greyish-green column. The flowers are small, in branching cymes on a slender stem which arises from the top of the column. This plant was regarded by Harvey as *C. deltoidea* Thunb., but it is not that species, and was renamed *C. arta* by Schonland.

C. ausiensis Hutchinson. V. (The plant was named by Dinter *C. hofmeyeriana*, but no description was given, so the name is invalid). South-West Africa, near Aus.

A low-growing plant with a stout, branching, woody stem, each branch ending in a close rosette of narrow, pointed, succulent leaves, rounded at the back, with white hairs on the surface and edges. Flowers white, in a close cyme on a slender stem arising from the centre of the rosette.

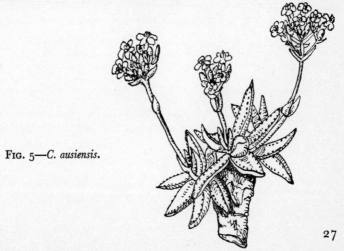

FIG. 5—*C. ausiensis.*

27

C. barbata Thunb. IV. South Africa, in dry Areas. Plate 1, *f*.

A rosette plant, the broad, pointed, recurving leaves decreasing in size towards the centre, green with long white hairs on the edges. From the centre rises a tall spike closely set with pairs of small leaves united at their base; in the axils of the upper ones the stemless flowers develop. The rosette dies after flowering, but new ones may be produced at the base.

C. barklyi N.E.Br. VII. Namaqualand.

This plant closely resembles *C. teres* (see Plate 8, *c*), but the leaves are without the transparent edge; this seems to be a variable feature, and the two plants may be the same species.

C. bolusii Hook. f. is now regarded as a synonym of *C. cooperi* (q.v.).

C. brevifolia Harv. IV. Namaqualand. Plate 7, *a*.

A shrubby plant, the stems woody at the base. The leaves are narrow, pointed, concave on the upper surface, convex below, glaucous with red tips. The white flowers are in a terminal corymb. It is closely allied to *C. rupestris*, but, despite its specific name, the leaves are longer and narrower. It was renamed *C. pearsonii* by Schonland, but it has been shown by Adamson that this name is not required.

C. capensis L. II. Cape Peninsula. Plate 2, *a*.

Sometimes called *C. septas* Thunb., this plant is rather variable. It is one of the few Crassulas that forms a tuber, the leaves dying down annually. The leaves may be larger than those shown in the illustration, but they are generally circular with a crenate edge. It should be kept dry after flowering, but is not easy in cultivation.

C. cephalophora Thunb. VI. Cape Province Thunb. VI. Cape Province, Basutoland, Orange Free State.

This plant is somewhat variable according to the district from which it comes; the leaves are broadest in the middle, flattish above, convex below and covered with minute hairs, larger along the edges. They are greyish-green, arranged in a basal rosette. The flowering stem is 10–12 in. high with small bunches of whitish flowers in the upper pairs of bracts.

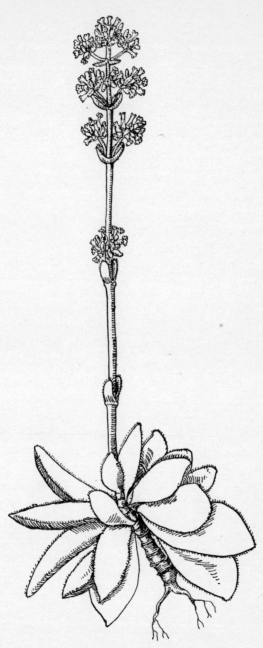

FIG. 6—*C. cephalophora.*

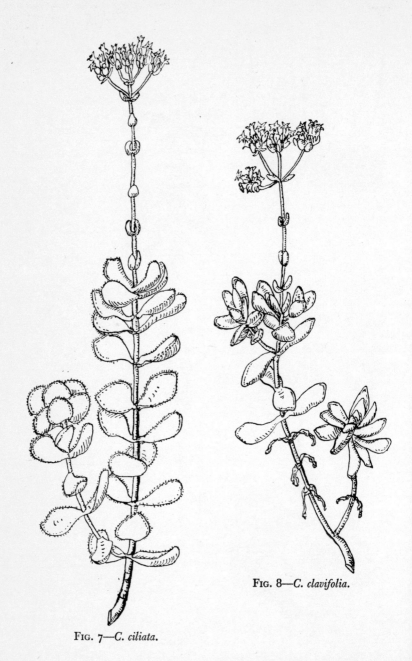

FIG. 7—*C. ciliata.*

FIG. 8—*C. clavifolia.*

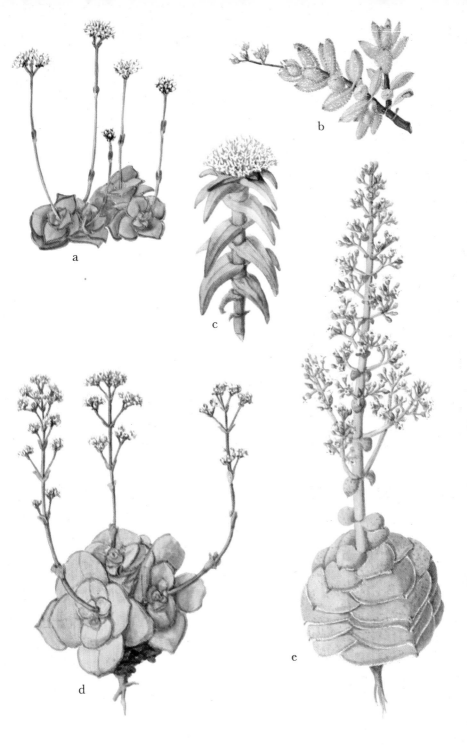

PLATE 3   a) *C. gillii*   c) *C. laticephala*   e) *C. hemisphaerica*
            b) *C. hystrix*   d) *C. intermedia*

PLATE 4   a) *C. nemorosa*   c) *C. mesembryanthoides*   e) *C. obvallata*
           b) *C. marginalis*   d) *C. mesembrianthemopsis*

C. ciliata L. V. Cape Province.

A small erect shrub with roundish leaves tapering to the base, the edges ciliate and with a red line; the small yellow flowers are in a branched inflorescence terminating the stem.

C. clavifolia (E. Mey.) Harv. Cape Province.

A small shrub with woody stems and narrow, spatulate leaves, green with a red edge; the small white flowers are in branching cymes. Allied to *C. anomala*.

C. columella Marl. et Schonl. IV. Plate 1, *e*.

A small shrub branching from the base, the stems hidden by the closely packed, succulent leaves, which are thick, pointed and olive green or brownish. The flowering stem is several inches high, branching at the apex, with several cymes of whitish flowers with hairy calyxes. Does not die after flowering.

C. columnaris Thunb. VII. Cape Province, in dry areas.
Plate 1, *d*.

This is a very compact plant; the leaves are wide, short and incurved, so that they form low columns; they are usually green with a paler edge, but may be brownish. The white flowers are borne in a close, terminal, almost stemless head. The plant dies after flowering. Should be kept in a sunny position and dry until the flowers begin to appear, otherwise the stem may become elongated.

C. comptonii IV. Hutchinson. Cape Province. Plate 2, *b*.

A small-growing plant with oblong leaves, flat on the upper surface, convex and hairy on the lower, held in close rosettes on very short, stout, woody stems. The close heads of yellow flowers are carried on red stalks.

Fig. 9—*C. conjuncta.*

C. conjuncta N.E.Br. IV. Eastern Cape Province.

This species is related to *C. perforata*; the leaves are closely joined in pairs, arranged alternately up the stem, ovate, tapering to a point, thickish, glaucous blue with a red edge and ciliate. The leaf-pairs decrease in size in the upper part of the stem, which terminates in stalked cymes of white flowers.

C. cooperi Regel. IV. Transvaal.

At one time two plants were in cultivation known as *C. cooperi* and *C. bolusii*, but the differences between them were never very marked nor very consistent, and they should be regarded as belonging to one variable species. The name *C. cooperi* was given by Regel in 1874 and therefore has precedence over *C. bolusii* given by Hooker fils in 1875. The leaves are in a loose rosette, slender, green with reddish dots and cilia along the edge. The flowers at the top of a leafy stem are white flushed with red and with deep red sepals. The plant should not be overwatered, or it may become long and straggly; a sunny position is best to bring out the colour. *C. cooperi* var. *major* is similar but rather larger and has been named *C. picturata* Boom.

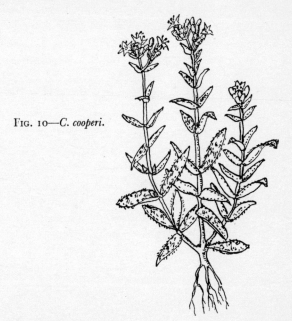

Fig. 10—*C. cooperi.*

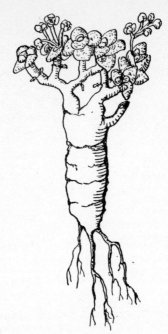

Fig. 11—*C. corallina*.

C. corallina Thunb. I. South-West Africa.

The plant frequently cultivated under this name is *C. dasyphylla* Harv. (q.v.); the true *C. corallina* Thunb. is the same as the plant later named by Schonland *C. simiana*, so that name should be dropped (see p. 20). It is characterised by the stout rootstock, from which arise short, more or less erect branches which do not root down even if they touch the soil. The leaves are small, short, broad and thick, the lower half of the upper surface concave, whitish, dotted with red, and are closely packed together; the small flowers are in terminal clusters on short stalks.

C. cordata Thunb. II. South-East Africa to Natal.

A slender branching shrub up to 12 in. (30 cm.) high; the heart-shaped leaves are pale in colour, powdery, with a reddish edge. The small, star-shaped, whitish flowers are carried on slender stems in a loose, branched inflorescence, where adventitious buds often form, which are useful for propagating. This plant prefers a warmer position in winter.

36

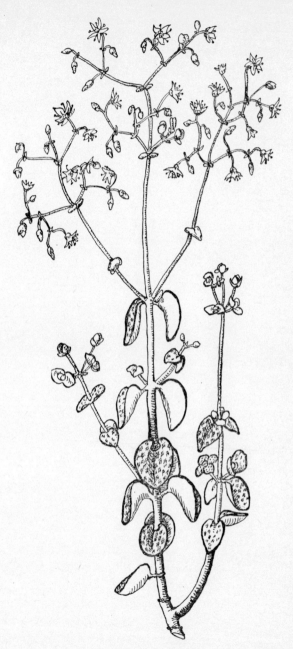

Fig. 12—*C. cordata.*

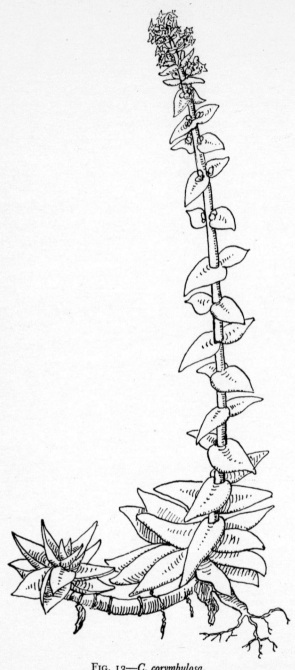

FIG. 13—*C. corymbulosa.*

C. cornuta Schonl. et Bak. f. IV. South-West Africa and Namaqualand. Plate 2, *c*.

This small plant branches from a woody base; the stems are hidden by the close-packed, triangular shaped, very succulent leaves, broad at the base, flat above, very convex below, ending in a point. The colour is whitish with a red edge and the surface is papilose. The tiny flowers are white, in small cymes on long, slender, reddish stems.

C. corymbulosa Link et Otto. IV. South-East Cape Province to Uitenhage.

An attractive plant forming clumps; it varies considerably, though the chief features are constant. Before flowering the leaves are crowded together at the base; they are slender, narrow, pointed, fairly thick, green with red colouring chiefly on the back and with, as a rule, cilia along the edge. At flowering time the stem elongates, carrying up some of the basal leaves to a height of 8–10 in. (20–30 cm.), the pairs of leaves decrease in size upwards, and the little white flowers in small cymes appear, almost stemless, in the axils of the upper leaf-pairs. After flowering new rosettes form at the base.

C. dasyphylla Harv. I. Eastern Cape Province.

This species has been in cultivation as *C. corallina*, but it differs from that plant in not having a stout, woody root-stock, and the branches, which are more or less prostrate, send out roots along their length. The leaves are small, broad and thick, closely packed and greenish with white markings. The flowers are produced at the tops of the stems from the axils of the leaves and are white; the petals are recurved and rather larger than those of *C. corallina* (q.v.).

FIG. 14—*C. dasyphylla.*

39

C. deceptrix Schonl. IV. Cape Province and Namaqualand.
Plate 2, *e.*

This is a small plant, often with a single stem, but it may branch at the base; the upper surface of the leaves is flat, the lower surface very convex with a keel. The colour is greenish grey and the surface marked with a raised network of lines. The loose inflorescence is about 2–3 in. (5–7½ cm.) high, the stem being reddish.

C. decipiens N.E. Br. is a synonym of **C. tecta** Thunb. (q.v.).

C. deltoidea Thunb. IV. Cape Province and Little Namaqualand.

C. deltoidea Harv. is not the same plant, see under *C. arta* Schonl. *C. rhomboidea* N.E. Br. is a later name for *C. deltoidea* Thunb. and therefore not valid.

A small, shrubby plant branching from the centre, the branches tending to be prostrate. The leaves are narrow, pointed, thick and close together, bluish grey in colour. The terminal inflorescence is a loose panicle on a short red stem, and the white flowers are marked with red dots at the base of the petals.

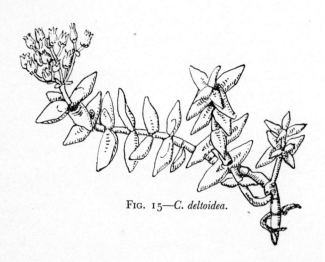

FIG. 15—*C. deltoidea.*

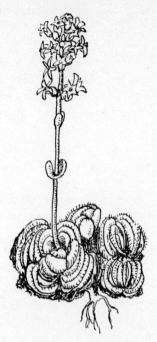

FIG. 16—*C. eendornensis*.

C. eendornensis Dint. nom nud. VI.

Plants under this name are sometimes found in collections, but since Dinter gave no description of the plant, the name is not valid. The plant is the same or closely allied to *C. interrupta* E. Mey., which is a very variable species.

C. ericoides Haw. IV. South Africa in mountainous regions.

The true plant is rare in cultivation, but *C. lycopodioides* forma *purpusii* Jacob. is sometimes found under the name *C. ericoides* Hort.

C. erosula N.E.Br. V. Cape Province and Namaqualand.

A small plant with long, narrow leaves, flat on top, convex below, dark green with a red edge. The flowering stem is long and slender branching towards the top and carrying several bunches of small white flowers.

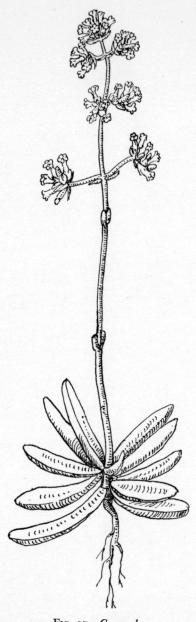

FIG. 17—*C. erosula.*

Fig. 18—*C. fragilis.*

C. falcata Wendl. IV. South-East Cape Province to Natal. Plate 2, *d*.

This is the most handsome of all the Crassulas, being a large plant up to 1 ft. (30 cm.) or more in height, with large, bluish grey leaves and a conspicuous inflorescence of scarlet flowers. The leaves are sickle-shaped and turned on edge. The stout flower stem is pinkish below, but becomes almost scarlet like the flowers where it branches to form a large, flattish inflorescence. It can be propagated by stem or leaf cuttings.

C. fragilis Schonl. VI. Cape Province.

A shrubby, branching plant with a woody stem which breaks easily, hence the name. The leaf-pairs are not very close together; the leaves are slender, blunt, narrowing to the base, green with soft white hairs. The inflorescence is about 6 in. (15 cm.) high and the white flowers are in compact cymes on long stems.

C. gillii Schonl. IV. South-East Africa. Plate 3, *a*.

This plant is related to *C. orbicularis* but smaller; the broad, pointed leaves, green with a reddish band near the ciliate edge, diminish in size towards the centre of the flattish rosette; it forms clumps. The flower stem is long and slender, terminating in several compact heads of small white flowers.

C. grisea Schonl. IV. Cape Province, Little Namaqualand.

A low, shrubby plant with narrow, pointed leaves united at the base, flat on top, convex below, greyish-green. The inflorescence is terminal, branching at the top, the small white flowers several together in small cymes.

C. hemisphaerica Thunb. IV. South-West Africa. Plate 3, *e*.

A rosette plant, the leaves being fairly large, wide at the base with pointed tips, recurved, the edge ciliate. From the centre rises a much branched inflorescence carrying small white flowers; the leafy bracts from which the branching flower stalks emerge are much smaller than the foliage leaves. The rosette may take several years to produce a flower spike, after which it dies, but basal offsets are sometimes formed which will develop into full-sized rosettes and flower several years later.

44

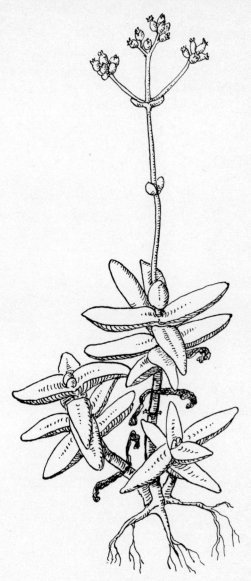

Fig. 19—*C. grisea.*

C. hystrix Schonl. V. Namaqualand. Plate 3, *b*.

A low shrubby plant with a woody, branching stem. The leaves are flat on the upper surface, very convex below, green with red tips, the whole covered with short, white, bristly hairs. The tiny yellow flowers are carried on short red stems at the tips of each branch. There is a superficial resemblance to the Mesembryanthemum, *Delosperma echinatum*.

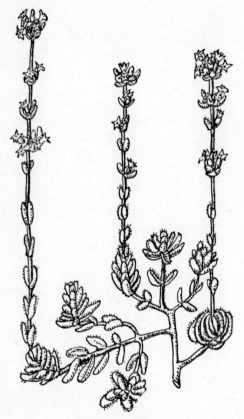

Fig. 20—*C. interrupta*.

C. intermedia Schonl. IV. South-West Africa. Plate 3, *d*.

This plant is closely allied to *C. rosularis* and forms similar flat rosettes which, when a number are produced on one root, tend to be close-packed and more vertical than horizontal. The leaves are broad at the base, short and pointed with horny cilia along the edge. The flowering stems are slender, with cymes of small white flowers from the upper bracts.

C. interrupta E. Mey. V. South-West Africa.

A small plant with the leaves closely packed in rosettes at the end of short, woody branches; the leaf edges are ciliate. The inflorescence is 2–3 in. (5–9 cm.) high, with a few white flowers in the axils of the upper bracts. The more compact *C. eendornensis* is probably only a form of this plant.

C. justus-corderoyi Jacobs. et v. Poelln. IV.

The origin of this plant is uncertain; in the early 1930s it was regarded as a hybrid that had arisen in the collection of succulent plants belonging to Mr. Justus Corderoy and was so regarded by Dr. N. E. Brown, who gave it the name *C. 'Justus Corderoy'*; under this name it was listed in Neale's Catalogue, 1935 and 'Said to be a hybrid. Dark green-brown, narrow leaves, pale pink flowers'. Later Jacobsen and von Poellnitz described it as a species. The leaves are crowded together at the base, short, narrow, thick, upper surface flat, lower rounded, dark green with red markings, hairy. The flowers are pink or red.

C. lactea Ait. II. Natal, Transvaal.

A plant with stout stems, generally procumbent, each ending in a loose rosette of large, obovate, green leaves which are pointed at the tip and with a line of white dots round the edge. The inflorescence is some 5–6 in. (12–15 cm.) high, branching and bearing a number of fair-sized, white, star-shaped flowers which are produced in winter. This makes an excellent house plant for the winter months and can be put out in the garden in the summer, if required; the best position would be in partial shade, not too damp.

47

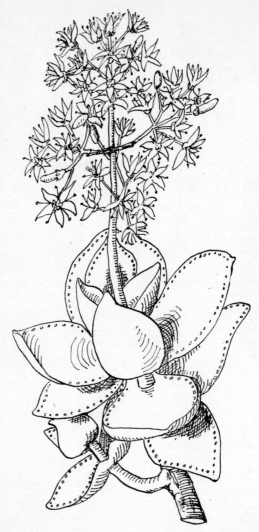

Fig. 21—*C. lactea.*

PLATE 5   a) *C. orbicularis*   c) *C. quadrangula*   e) *C. perforata*
           b) *C. triebneri*   d) *C. quadrangularis*

PLATE 6   a) *C. portulacea*   b) *C. pyramidalis*   c) *C. platyphylla*

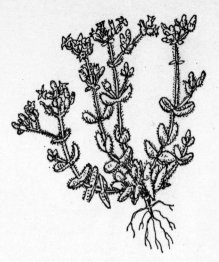

Fig. 22—*C. lanuginosa.*

C. lanuginosa Harv. VI. Cape Province.

An inconspicuous little plant that becomes woody at the base; the small leaves are semi-cylindrical and covered with soft hairs. The tiny white flowers are borne in small cymes in a branching inflorescence. It prefers a shady position.

C. laticephala Schonl. VIII. Cape Province. Plate 3, *c*.

A compact plant with a short, succulent stem 3–4 in. (7–10 cm.) long, related to *C. columnaris*, but instead of wide, incurving leaves those of *C. laticephala* are narrower; they embrace the stem but taper to a point, are strongly recurved and packed in four vertical rows. The close head of white flowers at the top of the stem also resembles that of *C. columnaris*.

FIG. 23—*C. lycopodioides.*

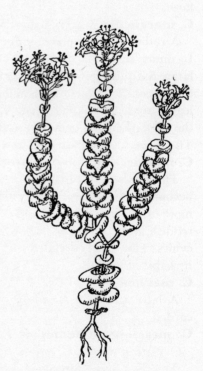

FIG. 24—*C. marnierana.*

52

C. lycopodioides Lam. I. South-West Africa.

A small branching plant, the stem being hidden by the pointed leaves, wide at the base, which are close-packed and form a slender, four-sided column; the flowers, which are very small and yellow, are borne in the axils of the younger leaves. Plants imported from South Africa are apt to be very tightly grown and are sometimes copper-coloured, rather than the dark green more frequently seen in Europe. There are a number of different forms in cultivation, but they seem mostly to be aberrant types, which may be due to incorrect cultivation—too much water or resting at the wrong time of year. A number of them have been given cultivar or varietal names. Fasciated forms, also, are not uncommon, and there is also a variegated form.

C. marginalis Ait. II. Cape Province. Plate 4, *b*.

A rather variable plant; some authorities include *C. pellucida* L. under the same name, the chief difference being that the latter has pink flowers. Usually the plant grows horizontally, the tips of the branches becoming erect at flowering time. The leaves are heart-shaped, green with a line of white dots round the edge, the pairs being more than the length of a leaf apart. The flowers are star-shaped and white.

C. marnierana Huber et Jacobs. IV. Cape Province.

The stems of this little plant may be erect when young but become prostrate and woody with age; the leaves are blunt, more or less heart-shaped and very thick, bluish but becoming reddish in the sun. The little white flowers are in short-stalked cymes. This plant is related to *C. rupestris*, but quite distinct in its habit of growth.

C. massonii Brit. et Bak. f.

A later name for *C. alpestris* and therefore should be discarded.

C. mesembrianthemopsis Dint. VII. South West Africa. Plate 4, *d*. Syn. *C. rapacea* Schonl. (see p. 21).

This is a most attractive little rosette plant with a stout woody root but almost stemless. The leaves are fleshy, triangular in section, erect with flattened tips, greyish-green and,

in nature, little more than the tips show above the sand. The white flowers are stemless and are crowded into the centre of the rosette. It should be rested in the summer and given a rather sandy soil.

C. mesembrianthoides Dint. et Berg. has been renamed *C. schoenlandii* Jacobs. (see p. 65).

C. mesembryanthoides (Haw.) D. Dietr. V. Cape Province. Plate 4, *c.* Syn. *C. trachysantha* Harv. (see p. 21).

This is an erect, shrubby plant growing to 1 ft. or more in height; it branches chiefly near the base, and the stems are woody below, ending in a branched inflorescence of whitish flowers. The pairs of leaves are some distance apart, and each leaf is cylindrical, tapering to a point and covered with bristly hairs.

C. milfordae Byles. IV. Basutoland.

A small plant collected by Mrs. Helen Milford in Basutoland, but it was not identified during her lifetime. It has been in cultivation for some time now and has proved hardy in a normal English winter but reluctant to flower. The leaves are thin and narrow and form rosettes at the ends of the stems which tend to be prostrate so that a loose clump is formed. It has been offered in the trade, but in some cases the name is incorrect. Its chief distinction to fame is its hardiness, for, even when it does flower, it is not a showy plant, the whitish flowers being held in small clusters at the ends of the stems.

54

FIG. 25—*C. milfordae.*

C. multicava Lem. II. Natal, Transvaal.

A fair-sized, shrubby plant with green leaves edged and dotted with red; they are about 1 in. across and rather more in length, narrowing to a stalk. The loose, branching inflorescence of white, star-like flowers is carried on a reddish stem and the buds are also red. It can be rooted from cuttings, but adventitious buds sometimes form in the inflorescence, which can be used for propagating the plant. It flowers early in the year and needs a fairly warm position in winter.

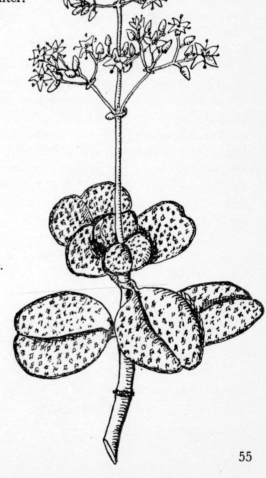

FIG. 26—*C. multicava.*

55

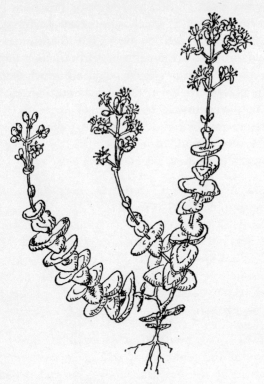

FIG. 27—*C. nealeana.*

C. nealeana Higgins. IV. Cape Province.

This small plant was imported with others from South Africa about 1930 by W. T. Neale and listed in his Catalogue (1935) as 'rupestris minima', and it was not until it flowered that it became obvious that it was not a form of *C. rupestris* though closely related to it. The stems are erect, but may become prostrate; the pairs of leaves are closely joined, ovate, very succulent, reddish green, and each stem ends in a branched inflorescence of small whitish flowers, more like that of *C. perforata* than *C. rupestris*. The same plant, still unnamed, was sent from South Africa in 1958, so that it probably is a true species and not, as some people have thought, a hybrid.

C. nemorosa Endl. II. South-West Cape Province. Plate 4, *a*.

An attractive little plant which is quite easy to grow and flower, though it does not appear to be widely distributed in cultivation. Below ground are small tubers from which short, bluish green stems arise bearing similar coloured, heart-shaped, little leaves. The flowers are borne on short stems, one, two or more together; they are white and held at right-angles to the stem. It is quite easy to grow if kept completely dry during the summer, when the leaves will all have died down; it propagates itself quickly by the formation of new tubers.

C. obliqua Ait. II. = *C. portulacea* var. *obliqua*. *C. obliqua* Andrews = *C. falcata* Wendl.

C. obliqua Ait. closely resembles *C. portulacea* in habit, but the leaves are generally more pointed and green without the red edge. It does not flower in this country, and its history is somewhat uncertain (see p. 22), so that it is probably best to regard it as a variety of *C. portulacea*, since this form appears to be unknown in South Africa now.

C. obvallata L. VI. South-West Africa. Plate 4, *e*.

The leaves of this plant are up to 2 in. (5 cm.) long, pointed and narrowing to the base, flat above, somewhat concave below. They are crowded at the base of the stem, but do not form a neat rosette. The tall inflorescence is branched towards the top and bears clusters of small white flowers.

C. orbicularis L. IV. Natal. Plate 5, *a*.

A rosette plant which makes offsets that are carried on slender, horizontal stems well away from the mother plant, where they root down so that a clump is soon formed. The flowers are white, held in a close head on a slender stem.

Fig. 28—*C. pellucida.*

C. pellucida L.

According to Jacobsen, a synonym of *C. marginalis*, but it differs in having rather larger flowers which are pink, not white, and smaller leaves without the white dots.

C. perfoliata L. IV. Cape Province to Natal.

A large plant with scarlet flowers, similar to *C. falcata*, but the leaves, instead of being sickle-shaped, are narrow at the base, tapering to a point, the upper surface concave and the lower convex. There is also a white-flowered form, var. *albiflora*.

C. perforata Thunb. IV. Cape Province, Karroo. Plate 5, *e*.

This species is variable according to the districts in which it grows. The essential characters are that the leaves are united in pairs, generally ovate, pointed, in some forms with a markedly ciliate edge. The stems are usually erect, but in some forms they become prostrate later; they branch chiefly from the woody base and terminate in a long, branching inflorescence with small yellow flowers in little cymes. When growing in dry areas the leaves are thicker, bluish with red edges and no cilia; in less dry areas the leaves are wider, green and the ciliate edge may be very marked.

C. perfossa Lam.

This name has been given to several plants, but is no longer in use, see p. 22.

Fig. 29—*C. perforata*, thin leaves with ciliate edge.

59

C. platyphylla Harv. VI. Cape Province. Plate 6, *c*.

Very similar to *C. obvallata*, but the leaves are wider, rounded at the top, narrowing to the base and forming a more compact rosette. It has been suggested that they may be extreme forms of one variable species.

C. portulacea Lam. II. Cape Province to Natal. Plate 6, *a*.

A shrubby plant which grows several feet high in South Africa. Small plants are attractive, but flowers are not usually produced on them until they are a foot or more high, with a stout woody trunk and several branches. The leaves are longer than broad, rounded at the top and narrowing to the base, glossy green with a red edge. The flowers are star-shaped, pink, about ½ in. across in loose panicles at the top of each stem. Since the plant flowers during the winter, a flowering-sized specimen is useful as a house plant; it can be put out of doors during the summer. See p. 26 for the confusion of the name with *C. argentea*.

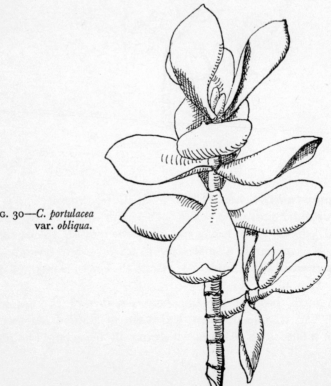

Fig. 30—*C. portulacea*
var. *obliqua*.

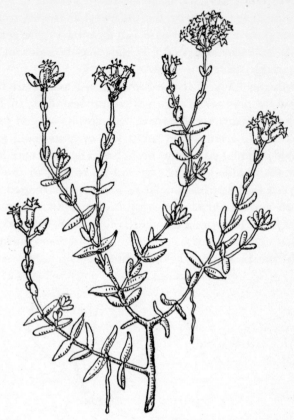

FIG. 31—*C. punctulata.*

C. punctulata Schon. et Bak. f. IV. Cape Province

A slender shrub only a few inches high with pairs of cylindrical, whitish green leaves spaced up the reddish, woody stems
which terminate in a small cluster of little, white flowers.

C. pyramidalis Thunb. VII. Cape Province, Namaqualand.
   Plate 6, *b*.

A small, branching plant about 4–5 in. (10–12 cm.) high
with flat, triangular, green leaves closely packed together to
form a four-sided column, which usually branches. The plant

61

superficially resembles some forms of *C. lycopodioides*, but the flowers are larger, white, in close, stemless heads at the ends of the branches.

C. quadrangula Endl. VII. Cape Province. Plate 5, *c.*

Very similar in the arrangement of the leaves to *C. pyramidalis*, but much stouter and less inclined to branch; it dies after flowering.

C. quadrangularis Schonl. IV. Cape Province, Karroo. Plate 5, *d.*

Although this name is sometimes confused with the previous one, the plants are quite distinct; instead of forming a column, *C. quadrangularis* makes a neat four-sided rosette; the leaves are broad at the base, short and pointed at the tip, green with a ciliate edge. The slender stem ends in a small head of little, white flowers.

C. radicans D. Dietr. VI. Cape Province. Plate 8, *d.*

This plant has branching, woody stems which are often prostrate, though the younger, leafy portions stand erect; the leaves are narrow, pointed, succulent, clasping the stem, which ends in a tall, slender inflorescence, with little bunches of white flowers towards the top only.

C. reversisetosa Bitter. IV. South-East Africa.

A small, rosette plant forming clumps; the leaves clasp the stem, which is reddish, and are pointed at the tip; the edges are

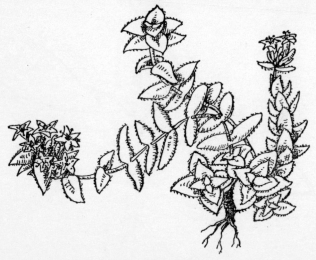

62

FIG. 32—*C. reversisetosa.*

ciliate. At flowering time the stems lengthen and bear at the top
a few white flowers in a small bunch.

C. rhomboidea N.E. Br. = *C. deltoidea* Thunb. (q.v.).

C. rosularis Haw. IV. Namaqualand to Natal.

The long, rather narrow leaves are held in a loose rosette,
from the centre of which the flowering stem arises bearing small
white flowers in little clusters towards the top.

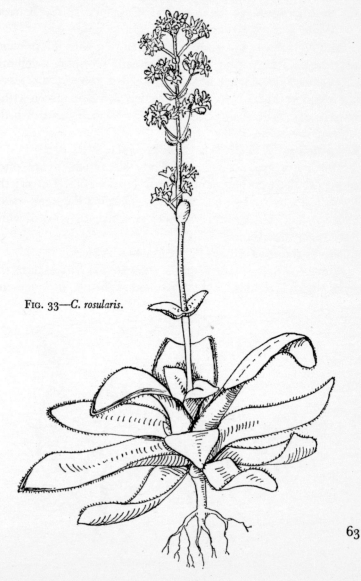

FIG. 33—*C. rosularis.*

C. rupestris Thunb. IV. Cape Province, Namaqualand. Plate
7, *b, c, d.*

This is a common shrub, but varies considerably over its wide
area of distribution. The leaves are closely joined in pairs,
usually ovate with a blunt tip and very thick. The upper surface is flat with a concave depression towards the stem; the
lower surface is very convex. The colour is usually green or
bluish green, but may be more or less reddish when growing in
dry positions. The flowers are in a branched corymb and may
be white or pink. Three different types are shown in Plate 7:

b. is the type which grows freely and, owing to the size and
weight of the leaves, the stems become prostrate, turning up at
the top when in flower.

c. is typical of the common type growing on the northern
slopes of the kopjes near Barrydale.

d. shows a variation of which two or three plants only were
found amongst acres of the dominant type shown in *c.*

C. sarcocaulis Eck. et Zehr. IV. Cape Province.

A small branching shrub with woody stems and small
glaucous green leaves; the flowers are in bunches at the top of
each stem and are red or sometimes white. The plant is hardy in
sheltered positions in Southern England.

FIG. 34—*C. sarcocaulis.*

Fig. 35—*C. schmidtii.*

C. saxifraga Harv. II. South Africa. Plate 8, *f.*

This is another of the tuberous-rooted *Crassulas*; they are interesting and very attractive when in leaf and flower, but not easy to keep alive for many years. The tuber must be dried off after the leaves have died down.

C. schmidtii Reg. IV. South-West Africa to Natal.

The names *C. impressa* N.E.Br. and *C. rubicunda* Hort are synonyms.

A small, branching shrub about 4 in. high. The erect, bristly stems bear long, narrow, pointed leaves, green above and brownish below with markedly ciliate edges. The branched inflorescence bears deep red flowers in winter.

C. schoenlandii Jacobs. IV. South-West Africa. Plate 8, *b.*

This plant was originally known as *C. mesembrianthoides* (see p. 21); it is a small, shrubby plant with a woody, branching stem and very succulent, ovate leaves crowded at the top, green or reddish; the small, carmine flowers are borne in a loose, terminal inflorescence.

65

C. simiana Schonl. is a synonym of *C. corallina* Thunb. (q.v.).

C. socialis Schonl. IV. Cape Province. Plate 8, *e*.

This is a very small rosette plant which forms mats; the bright green leaves, pointed at the tips and wide at the base, are in square rosettes, and from the centre of each a short, slender stem carries a small bunch of white flowers. It is a winter grower and should be put in a shady position when resting in summer but not kept completely dry.

C. spathulata Thunb. II. Cape Province to Natal.

A prostrate plant with heart-shaped, green leaves whose edges are finely crenate, and with distinct petioles, the pairs being $\frac{1}{2}$–1 in. apart. The stem terminates in a short, wide inflorescence of star-shaped flowers, white with crimson markings; the flowering time is late winter and spring. This species makes a useful house plant and can be grown in a pan or a hanging basket.

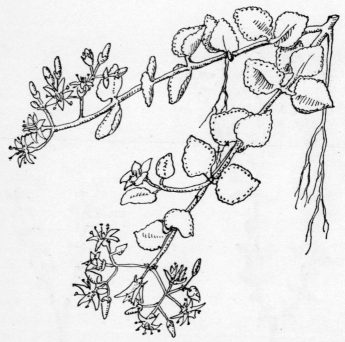

FIG. 36—*C. spathulata.*

PLATE 7   a) *C. brevifolia*   c) *C. rupestris*   d) *C. rupestris*
            b) *C. rupestris*

PLATE 8   a) *C. tecta*   c) *C. teres*   e) *C. socialis*
               b) *C. schoenlandii*   d) *C. radicans*   f) *C. saxifraga*

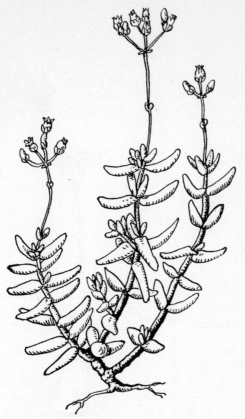

Fig. 37—*C. subaphylla.*

C. subaphylla (Eck. et Zehr.) Harv. V. South-West Cape
Province.

A small, woody, branching shrub with narrow, pointed succulent leaves, flat on the top, very convex below. The pairs are not
close together. The white flowers are few in number, carried on
a slender stem.

C. tecta Thunb. V. West Cape Province. Plate 8, *a.*

The plant is sometimes known as *C. decipiens,* a later name
given by N. E. Brown. The very thick leaves, broad and
rounded at the top, narrowing to the base, are greyish green
covered with numerous papillae. The flowers are white in close
bunches at the top of a stout stem.

E

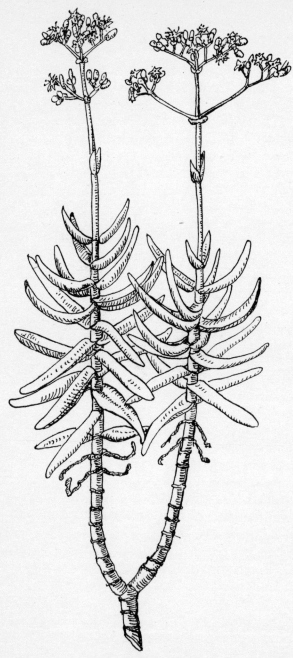

Fig. 38—*C. tetragona*.

C. teres Marl. VIII. South-West Africa. Plate 8, *c*.

This plant is very similar to *C. barklyi* and has been regarded as a possible hybrid. The leaves are broad, rounded at the top, incurved and closely packed up the stem to form a column which is surmounted by a terminal head of stemless, white flowers.

C. tetragona L. IV. East Cape Province.

This erect shrub branches chiefly from the base, and the stems may attain a considerable height. The leaves are about 1 in. long, flat on the upper surface, very convex below, narrow, pointed, green and the younger ones are curved upwards; they are fairly close together on the upper part of each stem, the lower part being bare and woody. The small white flowers are in branching cymes.

C. tomentosa Thunb. V. South-West Africa to Cape Province.

This plant seems to be somewhat variable in size; the rosette I received from South Africa grew to be 5 in. in diameter before it sent up a flowering spike 2 ft. high, but there seems to be a smaller-growing type in cultivation. The basal leaves are broadly oval, forming a loose rosette; they are fairly thick, hairy on the surface and with ciliate edges. The leaves on the flowering spike are rather narrower and become progressively smaller; the tiny white flowers are in sessile bunches in the axils of the uppermost leaves.

C. triebneri Jacobs. (The name was given by Schonland but without a description.) IV. South-West Africa. Plate 5, *b*.

A small plant, branching from the base; the leaves are thick, concave below and flat on top, green with scattered dots, held in a rosette but farther apart and becoming smaller up the stem, which terminates in a branching inflorescence of small, white flowers.

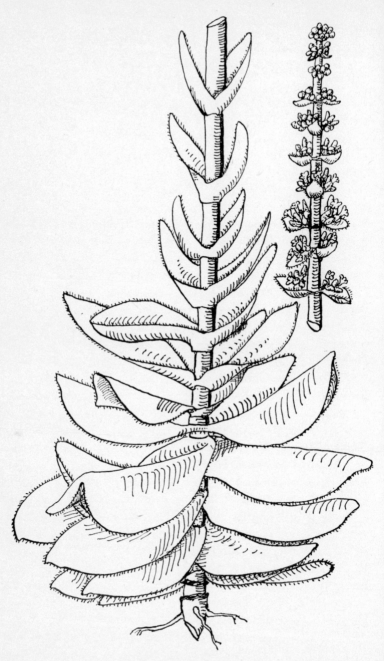

FIG. 39—*C. tomentosa.*

AUTHORS OF BOTANICAL NAMES

Ait.   William Aiton (1731–93), the first Curator of the Royal Botanic Gardens, Kew, author of *Hortus Kewensis* 1789, a catalogue of plants in cultivation at Kew which included a large number from the Cape.

Boom   Dr. B. K. Boom, of Wageningen, Holland.

Bak. f.   J. G. Baker (1834–1920), Keeper of the Herbarium at Kew from 1890 to 1899.

Diels   L. D. Diels, Professor of Botany at Marburg, Germany.

Dint.   Prof. Kurt Dinter, a German Professor at Dahlem who, with his wife, collected plants in South-West Africa for over forty years, and became Government Botanist of German South-West Africa.

Eckl. et Zehr.   C. F. Ecklon (1795–1868) and Karl Zehyer (1799–1868) collected extensively in South Africa, many of the plants being exported to Europe commercially. They published a list of the plants discovered.

E. Mey.   E. A. F. Meyer (1791–1851), Prussia.

Endl.   S. L. Endlicher (1804–1849), Professor of Botany at Vienna.

Haw.   Adrian Hardy Haworth (1772–1833) had a comprehensive collection of succulent plants near London and described them in several books.

Hook. f. Sir Joseph Dalton Hooker (1817–1911), who succeeded his father, William Jackson Hooker, as Director of Kew from 1865 to 1885.

Hutchison P. C. Hutchison of the University of California Botanic Gardens.

Jacobs. Hermann Jacobsen, until recently Curator of the Botanic Garden, Kiel, Germany.

L. Carolus Linnaeus (1707–78), a Swedish botanist who published *Species Plantarum* in 1753; this date is now accepted as the starting-point of binomial nomenclature.

Lam. J. B. P. A. de Monet Lamarck (1744–1829), a French Botanist at the Jardin du Roi, Paris.

Lem. Charles Lemaire (1800–71), a Belgian botanist interested in cacti and the botany of cultivated plants.

Link et Otto H. F. Link (1767–1851), Professor of Botany at Berlin, and F. Otto (1782–1856), Curator of Schoneberg, near Berlin.

Marl. Rudolf Marloth (1855–1931), a German chemist who went to South Africa in 1883 and became interested in the plants of that country; his *Flora of South Africa* was published in 1913 and completed in three more volumes.

Mill. Phillip Miller (1691–1771), Curator of the Chelsea Physic Garden and author of *The Gardener's Dictionary*.

N.E.Br. Nicholas Edward Brown (1849–1934) joined the staff of the Royal Botanic Gardens, Kew, in 1873 and worked in the Herbarium until 1930; he was particularly interested in South African plants.

Schonl. Selmar Schonland (1860–1940) went to South Africa in 1889 as Curator of the Albany Museum, Grahamstown. He was interested in the succulent plants and particularly in the Crassulas and wrote a comprehensive study of

the genus in *Transactions of the Royal Society of S. Africa*, Vol. XVII, 1929. (The name was originally spelt Schönland and is still so spelt on the Continent and in some plant names called after him, as *C. schoenlandii* Jacobs, but in the paper quoted above the author himself has spelt his name Schonland, not Schoenland or Schönland.)

Thunb. Carl Pehr Thunberg (1743–1822), a Swedish Botanist who went to South Africa and for some three years made a number of expeditions, being accompanied on two of them by Francis Masson, a collector for the Royal Botanic Gardens, Kew. The plants he discovered were described in his *Flora Capensis*.

Willd. Karl Ludwig Willdenow (1765–1812), Professor of Botany at Berlin, edited the *Species Plantarum* of Linnaeus, and his edition was published in five volumes from 1797 to 1810.

Index to Specific Names

Figures in bold type indicate descriptions.

abyssinica, 20
alba, 20
albiflora, 20
alpestris, **24**
alstonii, **24**
anomala, 18, **24**, 33
arborescens, 17, 20, **24**
argentea, 20, **26**, 60
argyrophylla, **27**
arta, 18, 21, **27**
ausiensis, **27**

barbata, 23, **28**
barklyi, **28**, 71
bolusii, 28, 38
brevifolia, **28**

capense, 18, **28**
cephalophora, **28**
ciliata, **33**
clavifolia, **33**
coccinea, 20
columella, **33**
columnaris, 19, **33**, 51
comptonii, 18, **33**
conjuncta, **35**
cooperi, 28, **35**
corallina, 17, 20, **36**
cordata, **36**
cornuta, **39**
corymbulosa, **39**

dasyphylla, 17, 20, 36, **39**
deceptrix, 16, 18, **40**
decipiens, 40

deltoidea, 21, 27, **40**

eendornensis, **41**
ericoides, **41**
erosula, 18, **41**

falcata, 11, 18, 20, **44**
fragilis, **44**

gillii, 16, **44**
grisea, 16, **44**

harveyi, 24
hemisphaerica, 18, **44**
hofmeyeriana, 27
hystrix, 18, **46**

intermedia, **47**
interrupta, **47**

justus-corderoyi, 47

lactea, 16, 17, **47**
lanuginosa, **51**
laticephala, **51**
lycopodioides, 11, 16, 17, **53**

marginalis, 17, **53**, 58
marnierana, **53**
massonii, 53
mesembrianthoides, 21, 54
mesembrianthemopsis, 16, 21, **53**
mesembryanthemoides, 21
mesembryanthoides, 21, **54**

milfordae, 54
multicava, 16, 55

nealeana, 16, 56
nemorosa, 16, 18, 57

obliqua, 22, 57
obvallata, 18, 57
orbicularis, 57

pearsonii, 28
pellucida, 58
perfoliata, 58
perforata, 12, 22, 59
perfossa, 22, 59
picturata, 35
platyphylla, 60
portulacea, 16, 17, 22, 26, 60
punctulata, 61
pyramidalis, 19, 23, 24, 61

quadrangula, 22, 62
quadrangularis, 22, 62

radicans, 18, 62
rapacea, 53
reversisetosa, 62
rhomboidea, 21, 40, 63
rosularis, 63
rupestris, 12, 16, 18, 22, 64

sarcocaulis, 18, 64
saxifraga, 65
schmidtii, 65
schoenlandii, 21, 65
septas, 28
simiana, 20, 36, 66
socialis, 18, 66
spathulata, 66
subaphylla, 69

tecta, 16, 18, 40, 69
teres, 19, 71
tetragona, 71
trachysantha, 21
triebneri, 71
turrita, 23